The Easy Piano Library

All-Time Greats

15 all-time greats arranged for Easy Piano by **Dan Coates**

Published 2002

Series Editor Anna Joyce
Production Editor Chris Harvey
Design IMP Studio

Music Arrangements Dan Coates
Cover Image © 2002 Getty Images

Dan Coates

As a student at the University of Miami, Dan Coates paid his tuition by playing the piano at south Florida nightclubs and restaurants. One evening in 1975, after Dan had worked his unique brand of magic on the ivories, a stranger from the music field walked up and told him that he should put his inspired piano arrangements down on paper so they could be published.

Dan took the stranger's advice—and the world of music has become much richer as a result. Since that chance encounter long ago, Dan has gone on to achieve international acclaim for his brilliant piano arrangements. His Big Note, Easy Piano and Professional Touch arrangements have inspired countless piano students and established themselves as classics against which all other works must be measured.

Enjoying an exclusive association with Warner Bros. Publications since 1982, Dan has demonstrated a unique gift for writing arrangements intended for students of every level, from beginner to advanced. Dan never fails to bring a fresh and original approach to his work. Pushing his own creative boundaries with each new manuscript, he writes material that is musically exciting and educationally sound.

From the very beginning of his musical life, Dan has always been eager to seek new challenges. As a five-year-old in Syracuse, New York, he used to sneak into the home of his neighbours to play their piano. Blessed with an amazing ear for music, Dan was able to imitate the melodies of songs he had heard on the radio. Finally, his neighbours convinced his parents to buy Dan his own piano. At that point, there was no stopping his musical development. Dan won a prestigious New York State competition for music composers at the age of 15. Then, after graduating from high school, he toured the world as an arranger and pianist with the group Up With People.

Later, Dan studied piano at the University of Miami with the legendary Ivan Davis, developing his natural abilities to stylize music on the keyboard. Continuing to perform professionally during and after his college years, Dan has played the piano on national television and at the 1984 Summer Olympics in Los Angeles. He has also accompanied recording artists as diverse as Dusty Springfield and Charlotte Rae.

During his long and prolific association with Warner Bros. Publications, Dan has written many award-winning books. He conducts piano workshops worldwide, demonstrating his famous arrangements with a special spark that never fails to inspire students and teachers alike.

As Time Goes By

Words and Music by
Herman Hupfeld

American Pie

Words and Music by
Don McLean

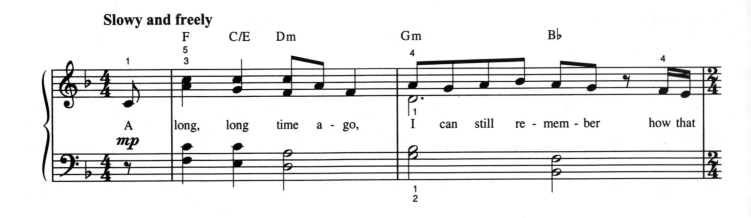

Verse 2:
I met a girl who sang the blues
And I asked her for some happy news,
But she just smiled and turned away.
I went down to the sacred store,
Where I heard the music years before,
But the man there said the music wouldn't play.
And in the streets, the children screamed,
The lovers cried and the poets dreamed.
But not a word was spoken;
The church bells were all broken.
And the three men I admire most,
The Father, Son, and Holy Ghost,
They caught the last train for the coast
The day the music died.
And they were singin' :
(To Chorus:)

The Greatest Love Of All

Words by Linda Creed
Music by Michael Masser

Desperado

Words and Music by
Glenn Frey and Don Henley

Over The Rainbow

Words by E Y Harburg
Music by Harold Arlen

Hotel California

Words and Music by
Glenn Frey, Don Henley and Don Felder

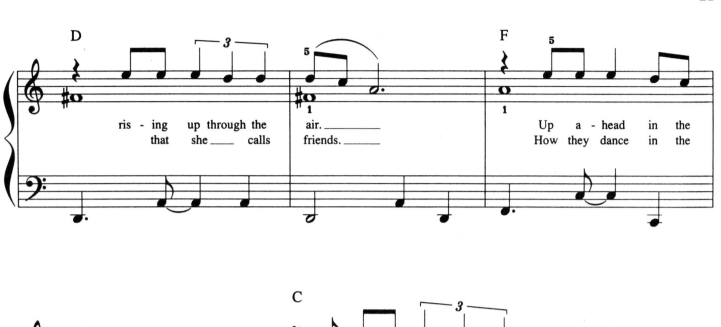

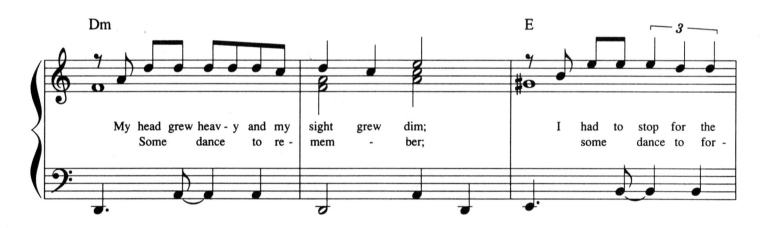

Lean On Me

Words and Music by
Bill Withers

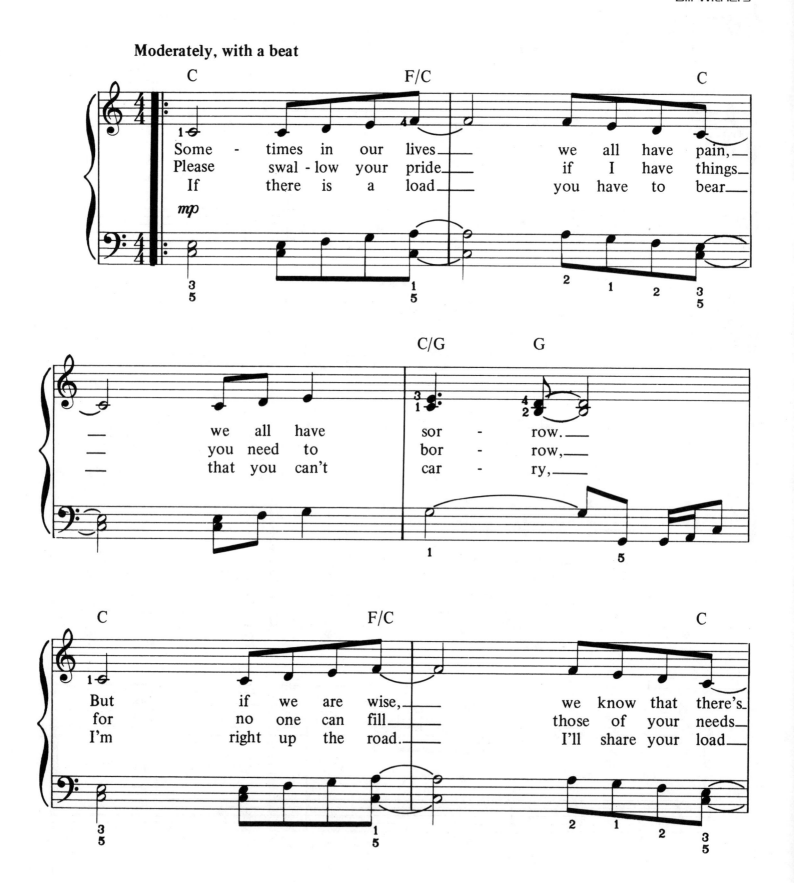

My Heart Will Go On

Words by Will Jennings
Music by James Horner

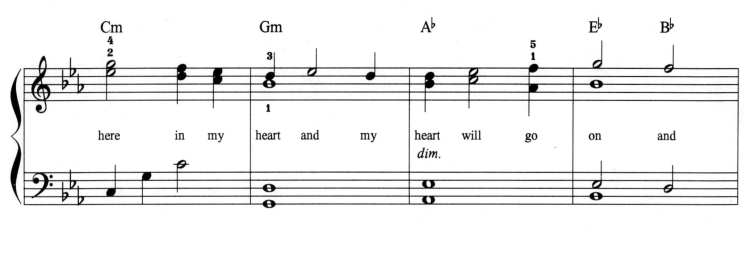

here in my heart and my heart will go on and

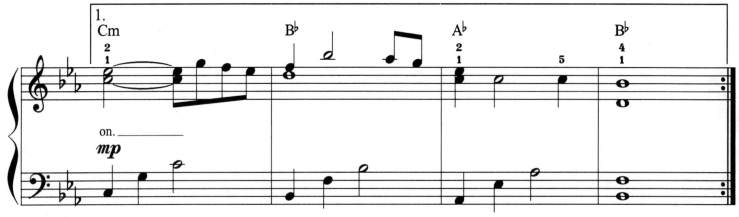

on.

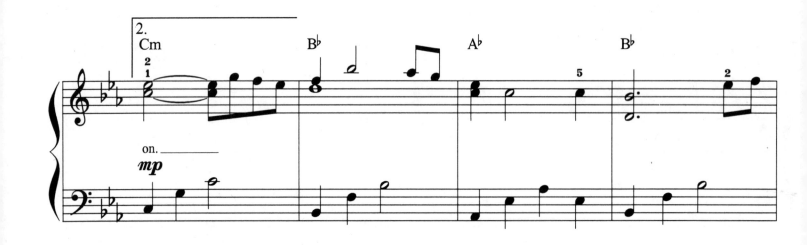

on.

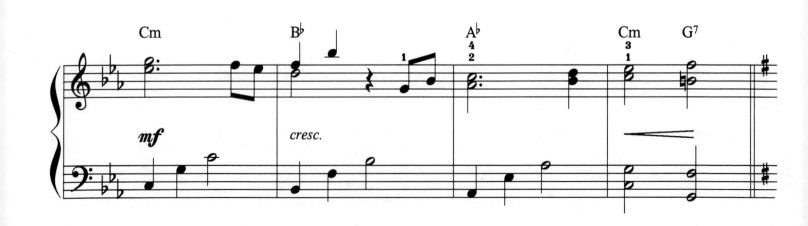

My Way

Original French Words by Gilles Thibaut
English Words by Paul Anka
Music by Claude Francois and Jacques Revaux

all, and I stood tall, and did it my way. I've

loved, I've laughed and cried, I've had my fill, my share of los - ing. And

now, as tears sub - side, I find it all so a - mus - ing. To

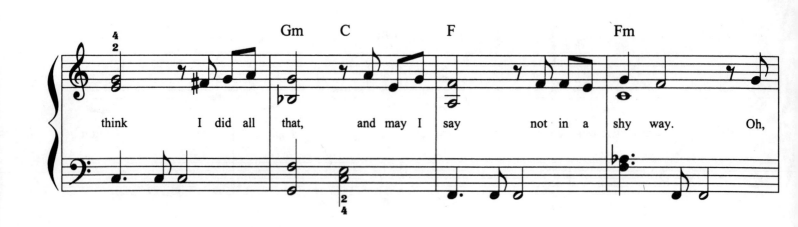

think I did all that, and may I say not in a shy way. Oh,

Sacrifice

Words by Bernie Taupin
Music by Elton John

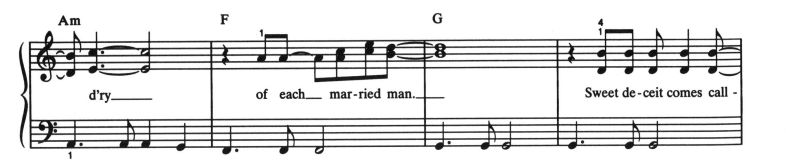

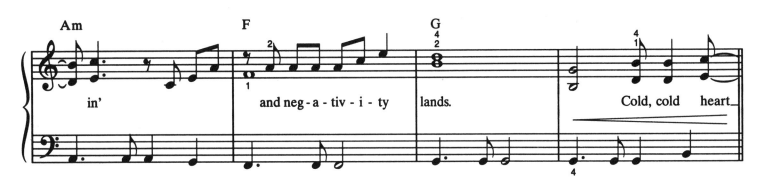

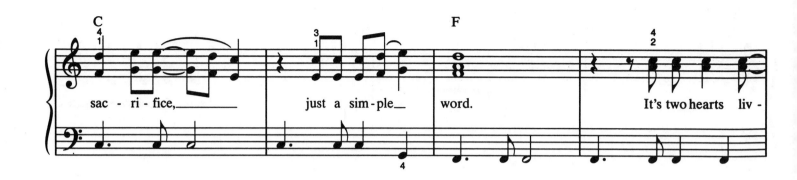

sac - ri - fice,_____ just a sim-ple_ word. It's two hearts liv -

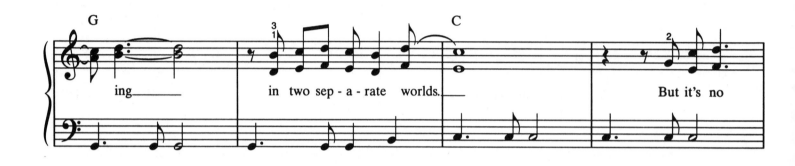

ing_____ in two sep - a - rate worlds._____ But it's no

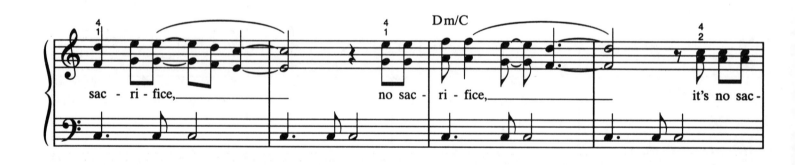

sac - ri - fice,_____ no sac - ri - fice,_____ it's no sac -

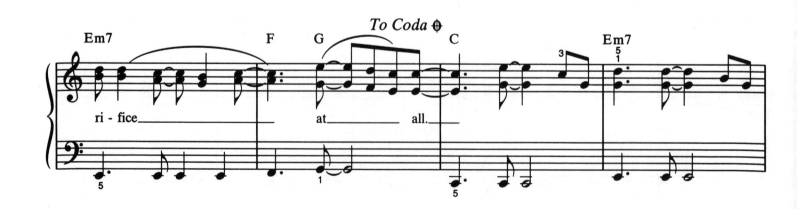

ri - fice_____ at_____ all._____

Verse 2:
Mutual misunderstanding
After the fact.
Sensitivity builds a prison
In the final act.
We lose direction,
No stone unturned.
No tears to damn you
When jealousy burns.
(To Chorus:)

Save The Best For Last

Words and Music by
Jon Lind, Wendy Waldman and Philip Galdston

Additional Lyrics

Sometimes the snow comes down in June,
Sometimes the sun goes 'round the moon.
Just when I thought our chance had passed,
You go and save the best for last.

Send In The Clowns

Words and Music by
Stephen Sondheim

Slowly, with expression

47

Stairway To Heaven

Words and Music by
Jimmy Page and Robert Plant

Theme From New York, New York

Words by Fred Ebb
Music by John Kander

When You Tell Me That You Love Me

Words and Music by
John Bettis and Albert Hammond